HISTORY & GEOGRAPH
SIX SOUTH AMERICAN CO

CONTENTS

Author: **Bess Morton**
Editor-in-Chief: Richard W. Wheeler, M.A.Ed.
Editors: Mary Ellen Quint, Ph.D.
     Merton B. Osborn, Ed.D.
Consulting Editor: Howard Stitt, Th.M., Ed.D.
Revision Editor: Alan Christopherson, M.S.

Alpha Omega Publications

a division of:
Bridgestone Multimedia Group

300 North McKemy Avenue, Chandler, Arizona 85226-2618

SIX SOUTH AMERICAN COUNTRIES

South America is in the southern part of the Western Hemisphere between the Atlantic Ocean and the Pacific Ocean. South America is the fourth largest continent in the world. This continent is a rich and beautiful portion of God's earth.

In this LIFEPAC you will learn about six countries of this great continent: Brazil, Colombia, Venezuela, and the three Guianas.

OBJECTIVES

Read these objectives. The objectives tell you what you should be able to do when you have successfully completed this LIFEPAC.

When you have finished this LIFEPAC, you should be able

1. To discuss the geography of Brazil, Colombia, Venezuela, and the three Guianas;
2. To tell about the wildlife in Brazil, Colombia, and Venezuela;
3. To discuss the people of Brazil, Colombia, Venezuela, and the three Guianas;
4. To state the major events of history in Brazil, Colombia, Venezuela, and the three Guianas;
5. To name major cities of Brazil, Colombia, Venezuela, and the three Guianas;
6. To name major industries of Brazil, Colombia, Venezuela, and the three Guianas; and
7. To describe present-day Brazil, Colombia, Venezuela, and the three Guianas.

VOCABULARY

Study these new words. Learning the meanings of these words is a good study habit and will improve your understanding of this LIFEPAC.

ascend (ä send´). To go up; to rise

banish (ban´ ish). To drive away; to dismiss.

bisect (bī´ sekt). To cut in two.

buccaneer (buk´ u nir´). A pirate.

candidate (kan´ du dāt´). One who seeks office.

cannibal (kan´ u bul). A person who eats human flesh.

classify (klas´ u fi). To arrange in groups or classes.

communication (ku myü nu kā´ shun). Giving information or news by speaking or writing.

conqueror (kong´ kur ur). One who subdues by force.

cruelly (krü ul ē′). Pitilessly; readily giving pain to others.

descendant (di sen′ dunt). Offspring; born into a family.

dictator (dik′ tā tur). One who exercises absolute authority.

emerge (i merj). To come up, to rise out, to come forth.

enable (en a′ bul). To make able; to give ability.

encourage (en kėr′ ij). To inspire with confidence; to give hope.

exception (ek sep′ shun). Leaving out; not a part of the general rule.

fortify (for′ tu fī). Strengthen for military defense.

hydroelectric (hī′ drō i lek′ trik). Generating electricity by water power.

hydroplane (hī drō plan′). A type of sea plane.

industry (in′ du strē). A branch of business, manufacture, or trade.

interior (in tir′ ē ur). Inside; something inland.

isolated (ī′ su lāt ud). Apart; separated.

junta (hün′ tu). A council, usually of citizens.

llano (yä′ nō). A wide plain.

manioc (man′ ē ok). A staple South American food from the cassava plant.

mythology (mi thol′ u jē). Study of myths or legends.

plantains (plan′ tuns). A banana-like fruit.

political (pu lit′ u kul). Pertaining to government affairs.

savanna (su van′ a). A grass land.

smuggler (smug′ lur). One who deals in goods secretly; against the law.

torrid (tôr′ id). Very hot.

traffic (traf′ ik). Coming and going of persons or vehicles.

vendor (ven′ dur). A seller; a peddler.

viceroyalty (vīs roi′ ul tē). Just below the top royalty (king).

Note: All vocabulary words in this LIFEPAC appear in **boldface** print the first time they are used. If you are unsure of the meaning when you are reading, study the definitions given.

Pronunciation Key: hat, āge, cãre, fär; let, ēqual, tėrm; it, īce; hot, ōpen, ôrder; oil; out; cup, pùt, rüle; child; long; thin; /ŦH/ for then; /zh/ for measure; /u/ represents /a/ in about, /e/ in taken, /i/ in pencil, /o/ in lemon, and /u/ in circus.

I. BRAZIL

Brazil, located on the eastern coast of South America, covers almost half the continent of South America. Its boundaries touch every other country of South America except those of Chile and Ecuador. Although people of the other countries have Spanish as their major language, most of the people of Brazil speak Portuguese.

Brazil is an important country not only because of its size, but also because of its future as an economic and **political** power in the modern world.

☐ **Review these objectives.**
1. To discuss the geography of Brazil;
2. To tell about the wildlife in Brazil;
3. To discuss the people of Brazil;
4. To state the major events of history in Brazil;
5. To name major cities of Brazil;
6. To name major industries of Brazil; and
7. To describe present-day Brazil.

☐ **Restudy these words.**

ascend	exception	manioc
bisect	hydroelectric	mythology
conqueror	industry	political
descendant	interior	savanna
dictator	llano	torrid

GEOGRAPHY

The geography of Brazil can be studied by looking at the regions, the major rivers, and the resources.

Regions. The major regions of Brazil are the Amazon Lowlands, the Central Highlands, the Sertão Region, the Southern Region, and the Coastal Plain.

The Amazon Lowlands cover the northern and western half of Brazil. They lie in the **Torrid** Zone near the equator where the air is hot and humid. Dense rain forests where the trees grow tall to reach the sunlight are found here. The Amazon River flows through this region. Small Indian villages are built near its banks in many places. Rubber trees and other forest products grow here in abundance.

The rain forests, the **savannas**, the rivers, and the plains (or **llanos**) of the Amazon River Basin abound in wildlife. In the forests live South America's largest

3

wild animal, the tapir, and its enemy, the jaguar. One-fourth of all the known kinds of animals in the world live in South America. Among some of the most unususal are the giant anteaters, the armadillos, and the sloths.

Among the many birds found here are parrots, macaws, and flamingos. Insects, such as butterflies, fiery bees, and fire ants, also abound.

Mountain Tapir

Do this activity.

1.1 Select one of the animals, birds, or insects mentioned. Look up additional information about it and write a paragraph, using complete sentences. Show your writing to a classmate.

_____

_____

_____

_____

_____

_____

_____

_____

_____

_____

_____

Teacher check _____

Initial   Date

The Central Highlands spread across Brazil from east to west except for the coastal mountains and the Coastal Plain. They make up most of the central part of the country. The climate of the Central Highlands is humid but cool. This cool climate is good for growing coffee.

The Sertão Region is a smaller area in the far northeast of Brazil. It extends out into the Atlantic "hump." It is a desert place where a drought occurs every ten years. Many people, however, live there and are loyal to their territory.

The Southern Region is **bisected** by the Tropic of Capricorn, and has the most favorable climate in Brazil. This region has many rich mines and large **industries**.

The Coastal Plain is a narrow strip of land along the east coast. Mountains **ascend** sharply and divide the coast from the rest of Brazil. Along this coast are located most of Brazil's large cities. Atlantic breezes help to make the weather tolerable, even near the equator.

Write the correct letter or word in each blank.

1.2   The Amazon Lowlands are located in _____ Brazil.
        a. northern
        b. southern
        c. eastern

1.3   The Amazon Lowlands are hot because they lie on or near the
        _____ .
        a. Arctic Circle
        b. Tropic of Capricorn
        c. equator

1.4   The people who build villages along the Amazon are called
        _____ .
        a. Amazonians
        b. Brazilians
        c. Indians

1.5   A rain forest has _____ .
        a. no trees
        b. grasses and bushes
        c. tall trees

1.6   A product of the rain forest is _____ .
        a. coffee
        b. rubber
        c. peaches

Complete this map activity.

1.7   Find the outline map of South America in the back of this LIFEPAC. Mark
        (or shade in with crayon or colored pencil) the Amazon Lowlands, the
        Central Highlands, the Sertão Region, the Southern Region, and Coastal
        Plain.

Complete these activities.

1.8   Choose from the following list five adjectives or phrases which describe
        the Central Highlands and write them in the blanks.
        central   southern   dry
        humid   cool   hot
        apple growing   coffee growing
        east to west   north to south
        a. _____   d. _____
        b. _____   e. _____
        c. _____

1.9   Circle the words that describe the Sertão Region.
           a. desert   b. northeastern Brazil
           c. humid   d. barren
           e. loyal citizen   f. drought
           g. southwest Brazil

1.10   A synonym is a word that has the same meaning as another word. For
           example, *ascend* is a synonym for *rise.* Write a synonym for each word.
           Use a dictionary if necessary.
           a. coast   _____
           b. sharply   _____
           c. large   _____
           d. tolerable   _____
           e. near   _____

Major rivers. Brazil has many rivers. The mighty Amazon, named after women in **mythology**, is the largest river in the world. The Amazon River flows from the Andes Mountains through the Amazon Lowlands to the Atlantic Ocean. One of its branches is the Negro River. Another branch is the Madeira River. If the Amazon and all its tributaries could be placed over a map of the United States it would cover about three-fourths of our nation. The Paraná River is in the south of Brazil. At the point on this river where Brazil and Paraguay meet, a **hydroelectric** plant has been built to provide power for several countries.

Complete this map-study activity.

1.11   Draw on the map of Brazil, the Amazon, Negro, Madeira, and Paraná rivers. Also label the Atlantic Ocean. Consult the maps available to you.

Resources. Brazil is a very large country with many mineral resources. Among the important mineral resources are iron ore, manganese, gold, diamonds, and bauxite. Manganese is a metal similar to iron. Bauxite is the ore from which aluminum is made.

Brazil also raises many important farm products. More coffee is raised in Brazil than in any other country. This industry supplies many workers with jobs. Brazil also raises sugarcane, cacao, (from which comes cocoa and chocolate), cotton, rice, corn, potatoes, and wheat.

Animals of commercial value raised in Brazil include hogs, cattle, and sheep. Cattle are raised in the south and south-central states. Sheep are raised in the Sertão Region.

Brazil's numerous rivers and streams provide a home for fish and furnish water power to make electricity. They also form an important network of water transportation to carry goods from the **interior** to the coastal ports.

In recent years, persons and industries moved into South America's interior. They cut down trees and leveled some of the rain forests, especially near the Amazon. In 1992, Brazil held an "Earth Summit" to discuss ways to solve this problem. People from 176 countries were there.

Complete the outline.

1.12   Read the section on Brazil's resources once again. Complete the outline
with information from this section.

Resources of Brazil

I. _____
    A. _____
    B. _____
    C. _____
    D. _____
    E. _____
II. _____
    A. _____
    B. _____
    C. _____
    D. _____
    E. _____
    F. _____
    G. _____
    H. _____
III. _____
    A. _____
    B. _____
    C. _____
IV. _____
    A. _____
    B. _____
    C. _____

PEOPLE

Nearly all the heavily populated areas of Brazil are within a hundred miles or less of the coastline. The remainder of the country is less densely populated. In studying the population of Brazil, you will be learning about the races of people in Brazil and about the social classes.

Race. Over one-half of the population of Brazil are people of European descent. The greatest number of these are Portuguese. Because so many people are of Portuguese descent, Portuguese is Brazil's official language.

Black slaves were brought from Africa in the eighteenth century. Their **descendants** make up the second largest portion of Brazil's population today. The Japanese began to come to Brazil in 1908. Indian natives retreated to the interior when they did not work out as slaves of the **conquerors**. Since Brazil has such a variety of cultural and racial backgrounds, it is less likely to have race prejudice than other places in the world.

Social class. People are conscious of class not only in Brazil, but also in much of South America. The landowners, the overlords, and the overseers of *fazendas* (plantations) or factories are the wealthy class. The poor often work for the overlords and the landowners. Many of these poor have migrated to the cities and live in *favelas*, or slums, that surround the cities. The Indians of Brazil's jungles may seem very poor to us. For the most part, however, they live well in the jungles or the rain forests.

Most people in Brazil are either very rich or very poor. Some changes are beginning to happen. In recent years large businesses have bought more and more of the plantations and the industries. They hire men and women to work and pay them wages just as employers do in other parts of the world. Some people are beginning to earn wages and are moving to better homes with better living conditions. These wage earners are joined by small farm owners who have managed to buy their own farms. Together they form a new class, the middle class. Very, very slowly a middle class is beginning to grow in Brazil that may someday change the way that both the rich and the poor now live.

Food. The main foods of the average Brazilian are rice, beans, and meat. **Manioc**, the root of the cassava plant, is ground into flour and used in many ways. *Feijoada*, the national dish, is made with beans and beef, sprinkled with manioc flour.

Fish dishes are enjoyed by those who live in the coastal towns. The meat of the sea turtle is especially delicious.

Children are fond of sugar cakes *(doces)* and soft drinks are consumed everywhere.

👉 **Complete these sentences by writing the correct answer in the blank.**

1.13   Most people of Brazil live _____ .
        a. in the jungle   c. in the mountains
        b. near the coast   d. on the desert

1.14   The official language of Brazil is _____ .
        a. English   c. French
        b. Portuguese   d. Chinese

1.15   Early settlers brought Blacks from Africa to be _____ .
        a. hired help   c. slaves
        b. landowners   d. overlords

👉 **Match these activities.**

1.16   _____ manioc   a. coastal towns
1.17   _____ fish   b. rice, beans, and meat
1.18   _____ *feijoada*   c. cassava plant
1.19   _____ main foods of Brazil   d. national dish
1.20   _____ sugar cakes   e. rubber
                                   f. *doces*

Use words from the Word Bank to complete this paragraph.

WORD BANK

modern	wages	big businesses
overseers	plantations	rich
factory	industries	middle class
land	poor	

1.21   The owner of the a. _____ would be b. _____ . The
people who worked for him were very c. _____ .
The d. _____ were richer than the workers in the
e. _____ . In f. _____ times
g. _____ own some of the h. _____ and
i. _____ . Some people work for j. _____ .
A new class, the k. _____ , is slowly growing in Brazil.

HISTORY

On April 22, 1500, Pedro Alvares Cabral discovered the land that today is Brazil. He claimed this land in the name of Portugal. This event took place about eight years after Christopher Columbus had sailed from Spain and discovered the New World. Cabral left this land nine days later on a voyage to India, but he left two men behind. One of Cabral's ships sailed back to Portugal with some Indian pottery, plants, some brightly colored parrots, and some logs. The logs were a highly valued wood known in Portugal as *pau brasil*. From this wood, Brazil got its name. A red dye was obtained from this brazilwood tree and became an important item of trade with Europe.

The first permanent settlement was made at São Vincente, a seaport near the present city of Santos, in 1532. The king of Portugal established thirteen captaincies on the east coast. By 1549 he had sent his first overlord to rule them. The capital of the first captaincy was Salvador. For more than a century after that, from 1554 to 1698, Brazil suffered many growing pains. São Paulo (1554) and Rio de Janeiro (1565) were founded after aspiring French colonists were driven out. The Dutch also had to be defeated and were removed in 1654. Gold was discovered in 1698 by eager Portuguese who were bearing their flag to the interior regions. Coffee seedlings from Europe were planted in the Coastal Plain and eventually would become one of Brazil's chief exports. Rio de Janeiro was made the permanent capital of Brazil in 1763 and remained so until 1960, a period of nearly 200 years.

Colonies all over the world were seeking freedom in the 1780's. Brazil was no **exception**. One early leader in the freedom movement was the man with the long name of Joaquim José de la Silva Xavier. His followers affectionately called him "Tiradentes," or the "tooth puller," because he was a dentist.

Match these columns by writing the letters in the proper blanks.

1.22 _____ red dye
1.23 _____ 1698
1.24 _____ 1565
1.25 _____ discoverer
1.26 _____ 1654
1.27 _____ freedom movement
1.28 _____ chief export

a. "Tiradentes"
b. coffee
c. Dutch removed
d. brazilwood
e. Rio de Janeiro
f. manioc
g. gold
h. Cabral

Portuguese empire. In 1807 King John VI of Portugal fled to Rio de Janeiro to escape Napoleon's attacks on Portuguese ports in Europe. He opened Brazil's ports to world trade. He also established a bank, a naval academy, a newspaper, a school of medicine, and a national library. Nine years later he became the king of Portugal and called his realm the United Kingdom of Portugal, Brazil, and Algarve. He did not return home, but ruled his kingdom from Brazil. Rio de Janeiro, therefore, became the first capital of a European country in the Western Hemisphere.

Independence. By 1821 King John had to leave for Portugal. He left his son, Dom Pedro I, to be regent of Brazil. By now King John's power was diminished. Portugal intended to reduce Brazil to colonial status. Dom Pedro I was greatly opposed to this action. On September 7, 1822, he received another order from the homeland. Angry, he tore the Portuguese emblem off his hat and proclaimed, "Independence or Death!" September 7 is celebrated as Brazil's Independence Day, a national holiday.

Dom Pedro I was crowned emperor of Brazil in 1822. By 1824 a new constitution was adopted making Brazil a constitutional monarchy. The United States, also in 1824, became the first nation to recognize the new Brazilian government. Other nations, even Portugal, followed. In four years, however, a boundary dispute forced Dom Pedro I to abdicate. Ten years later, in 1841, his son, Pedro, who was only fifteen years old, was crowned emperor of Brazil. Dom Pedro II proved to be wise and popular. He ruled for nearly fifty years. During that time he visited the United States. He abolished slavery in Brazil in 1888 and because of this, Dom Pedro II was removed from his throne a year later.

New republic. After Dom Pedro II was exiled to Europe, a movement toward real democracy was made in Brazil. In 1891 a democratic constitution, much like the United States Constitution, was adopted. Manuel Deodoro da Fonseca was the first elected president of Brazil. The provinces were made states. Many elected presidents served Brazil well, but in 1930, a **dictator** named Getúlio Vargas took over the government during a revolution. He abolished **political** parties and reigned until 1954.

Two years later Juscelino Kubitschek was voted the constitutional president of Brazil. During Kubitschek's term of office, the city of Brasília was built to open the interior of the country. Brasília was made the capital city in 1960. In 1966 the military took over the government of Brazil. In a military democracy only members of the military are elected president. General J. B. Figueiredo was elected in 1979. In 1985 civilian government was restored with presidential elections. The presidents have been: Fernando Collor de Mello, 1989; Itamar Franco, 1992; Fernando Henrique Cordoso, 1994.

Write *true* **or** *false.*

1.29 _____ In April, 1510, Cabral discovered Brazil.

1.30 _____ *Tiradentes* means *freedom lover.*

1.31 _____ King John of Portugal fled to Rio de Janeiro because Napoleon was attacking Portugal.

1.32 _____ King John fled to Rio de Janeiro in 1807.

1.33 _____ King John opened ports in Brazil to world trade.

1.34 _____ Brazil does not have any schools of medicine.

Choose words from the Word Bank to complete this paragraph.

WORD BANK
---

fifty
September 7, 1822
1841
hat
colonial
fifteen
five

slavery
constitutional
regent
Portuguese
constitution
monarchy

government
four
reduce
"Independence or Death"
Independence
abdicated

1.35 Dom Pedro I was first made a Portuguese a. _____ , but opposed the homeland's desire to b. _____ Brazil to c. _____ status. He became emperor of Brazil when he tore the d. _____ emblem off his e. _____ and shouted f. " _____ !" This event happened on g. _____ , the date now celebrated as Brazil's h. _____ Day. During Dom Pedro I's reign a i. _____ was adopted making Brazil a j. _____ k. _____ . The United States recognized the l. _____ of Brazil. Dom Pedro I only remained as king of Brazil for m. _____ years before he n. _____ . His son, Dom Pedro II was o. _____ years old at the time, but he was not crowned emperor of Brazil until he was p. _____ in the year q. _____ . He ruled for r. _____ years, but had to step down when s. _____ was abolished in the year 1888.

Answer these questions.

1.36 What other constitution did Brazil's democratic constitution resemble?

_____

1.37 How did Vargas differ from other presidents of Brazil? _____

_____

1.38 What was the name of the president who established Brasilia?

_____

11

CITIES

Brazil has many cities, each important in its own way. The cities of Brazil that we will study are São Paulo, Rio de Janeiro, Brasília, Manaus and Belém.

São Paulo. São Paulo, the largest city in Brazil, is much like New York City. People with many backgrounds live there. It is the closest large city to the coffee plantations and has many industries. One interesting place in São Paulo is the Butana Snake Institute, where scientists experiment with snake venom for the health of the world.

Rio de Janeiro. Rio de Janeiro is located about halfway down the Atlantic coast of Brazil. It is a colorful city and a major port of South America. For many years Rio de Janeiro was the capital of the country. Its harbor, with Sugar Loaf Mountain in the background, is considered by many to be one of the most beautiful harbors in the world.

Overlooking the city, high on top of Corcovado Mountain, stands the famous statue *Christ the Redeemer.* This beautiful statue is made of concrete and is flooded with brilliant lights at night. It can be seen from many miles away, reminding everyone that Christ has redeemed all men by His death and Resurrection.

Brasília. A few years ago, the government of Brazil decided to build a new capital in the wilderness. Under President Kubitschek's supervision, plans were drawn and a site was chosen. Workers cleared the land, built roads from the coast to the interior and a new, modern city began to arise. Some of the buildings have been built over pools of water and look as though they were floating.

Brasília was dedicated on April 21, 1960. Although some government buildings are not yet completed, the population has grown to more than 5,000,000.

Manaus and Belém. Manaus is an old city named after a tribe of Indians. It is located far up the Amazon. Manaus has no roads leading to it. A four-day journey is needed to reach Manaus by river steamer from the coast. Although Manaus is a jungle city, it has many buildings, both old and new. The most famous of its old buildings is the Opera House, built in 1896, when Manaus was a boom town as a result of the rubber trade.

Belém, a city on the Para River, is a major port for shipping forest and jungle products to other countries of the world. Its name is a shortened form of the word *Bethlehem.*

Complete this activity.

1.40   Read again the paragraph about the city of São Paulo. Choose synonyms for the words and write them in the blanks.

a. largest _____   d. closest _____

b. like _____   e. industries _____

c. people _____

 **Match the following activities.**

1.41	_____ Christ, the Redeemer	a.	rubber boom-town
1.42	_____ Belém	b.	President Kubitschek
1.43	_____ Brasília	c.	mountain overlooking Rio de
1.44	_____ Manaus		Janeiro
1.45	_____ Corcovado	d.	*Bethlehem*
		e.	famous statue
		f.	Sugar Loaf Mountain

FESTIVALS AND RECREATION

Carnival is the great holiday of Brazil, especially in Rio de Janeiro. Carnival begins forty-two days before the observance of Christ's resurrection. Parades, street festivals, and other events are held. Carnival ends in time for religious services the morning of seventh Wednesday before the observance of Christ's resurrection. Other Brazilian holidays are Independence Day, September 7, and St. John's Day, June 23. People go to the beaches during the hot months of December, January, and February. (South of the equator seasons are reversed.) Soccer is the most common sport in Brazil. Pelé is the country's most famous player.

 Complete this activity.

1.46   Look up *Ash Wednesday*, *Lent*, and *Carnival*, in your school encyclopedia. Tell how these three special times are related.

_____

_____

_____

_____

_____

_____

_____

_____

INDUSTRY

São Paulo, the fastest growing city in the world today, is in the heart of industrial Brazil. Rich farm land lies all around it. Water power is abundant and the climate is pleasant. For these reasons, local and foreign companies have built factories in or near São Paulo. Within a one-hundred mile radius of this city, dozens of smaller industrial cities have begun to grow. Of all the manufactured products that come from Brazil, more than half come from this area. Some of the more important goods manufactured here are food, clothing, medicines, steel and machinery, cement, paper, paint, furniture, autos, and tires.

Complete this activity

1.47   The fastest growing city in Brazil is _____ .

1.48   Many important goods are manufactured in the São Paulo area. Some of these goods are

a. _____ ,   d. _____ ,

b. _____ ,   e. _____ , and

c. _____ ,   f. _____ .

BRAZIL TODAY AND TOMORROW

When you have the opportunity to look at a Brazilian flag, you will notice that it is green, with twenty-two white stars forming the constellation of the Southern Cross on a blue circle with a gold diamond in the center. Across the blue circle are the words "Order and Progress" written in Portuguese. These two words, *order* and *progress,* seem to summarize the ambitions and the goals of the people of Brazil.

Schools.   Brazilian children begin school at age seven or eight. After five years of elementary studies, they begin junior high school. Discipline is very strict. No one talks unless he is asked to speak. Then, he stands by his seat and recites. The boys and the girls have separate classrooms. Courtesy is stressed in all classrooms.

Standards are high, and students must study hard to go on to higher grades. A great deal of homework is required. Marks for report cards come in numbers from 1 to 10 and a student must have an average of 5 to pass. If a students makes good grades during junior high and *colegio* (similar to high school in the United States), he may go on to the university.

Too few schools exist for the number of children. Brazil is trying to obey a new law stating that every town must have an elementary school. Schools are being built as fast as possible, and the hope is that soon no children will be without an education.

Transportation. Except for commerce on the rivers and ocean, transportation has been one of Brazil's greatest problems. Without air transportation, very little progress could have been made. Since Brasília has been built, more and more highways are branching out from central Brazil. Many more highways are needed. As the nation of Brazil grows, these progressive people will establish more airlines, and more and better roads.

Religion. Although the majority of Brazilians are Catholic, about a million and a half Protestants live in the country. Brazilians are free to follow the religion of their choice. Jesus said, "Go ye therefore, and teach all nations, baptizing them in the name of the Father, and of the Son, and of the Holy Ghost . . . ." Protestants are active in Brazil. Some Protestant missionaries live in villages with the Indians. Some are translating the Bible into native languages. Others are making Gospel recordings in the languages of the natives and sending them to missionaries free of charge. You can imagine the excitement when the natives hear God's Word coming back to them in their own language and spoken by someone from their own tribe. Christian aviation services fly natives and missionaries in and out of the jungles. Radio, too, is carrying the message of the Gospel to many who have not heard.

Recently the Director of Education for Brazil has ruled that all public school children in Brazil shall have a New Testament and shall study it in school. Christian organizations in the United States are having these New Testaments printed and sent to the schools as a gift of love to the children of Brazil.

Answer these questions.

1.49   What is the national motto on the Brazilian flag?

_____

1.50   What new law has been passed that will help children learn to read and write?

_____

_____

1.51   Do you think that this law will be difficult to carry out?

_____

_____

_____

1.52   What are three of the most used means of transportation in Brazil?

_____

1.53   What are three ways in which missionaries are bringing God's Word to the natives?

a. _____

b. _____

c. _____

1.54   Why are elementary school children of Brazil having an opportunity to read and study the New Testament?

_____

_____

_____

 Do this exercise on a separate piece of paper.

1.55   The following lists are names of people, products, or resources in Brazil. Choose one of them. Look up further information on your choice in a book or encyclopedia. Write a report of at least three paragraphs.

Heroes	**Plants**	**Resources**
Pelé, athlete	rubber trees	iron mountains
Antonio Lisboa	Brazil nuts	emeralds
crippled sculptor	ceiba tree	diamonds
Pedro Alvares Cabral	kapok	gold
Dom Pedro II	coffee	

 Teacher check _____

                     Initial   Date

 Review the material in this section to prepare for the Self Test. The Self Test will check your understanding of this section. Any items you miss on this test will show you what areas you need to restudy.

SELF TEST 1

Circle the correct answer (each answer, 2 points).

1.01   The Coastal Plain of Brazil has _____ .
         a. no cities
         b. only rocks
         c. many cities
         d. small villages

1.02   The Amazon Lowlands are hot because they are mostly at sea level right near the _____ .
         a. Arctic Circle   c. river
         b. Tropic of Capricorn   d. equator

1.03   The Coastal Plain is divided from the rest of the country by _____ .
         a. steep mountains   c. large rivers
         b. a snow cap   d. an isthmus

1.04   A word that means the same as another word is _____ .
        a. a synonym   c. a homonym
        b. an antonym   d. a verb

1.05   The basic meaning of the word amazon is _____ .
        a. great mountain   c. big river
        b. large woman   d. wide plain

1.06   A place that generates electricity from a river or other flowing water is
        a. _____ .
        a. growing industry   c. power company
        b. waterfall   d. hydroelectric plant

1.07   The largest animal in Brazil is the _____ .
        a. elephant   c. giraffe
        b. tapir   d. dog

1.08   A national dish made of rice, beans, and meat is called _____ .
        a. manioc   c. feijoada
        b. doces   d. turtle

1.09   Brazil is the largest producer in the world of _____ .
        a. rosewood   c. oranges
        b. coffee   d. vegetables

1.010   Over one-half of Brazil's population is descended from _____ .
        a. Europe, mostly Portugal   c. Mexico and central America
        b. Asia, mostly Japan   d. North America, mostly Canada

1.011   Blacks are in Brazil because _____ .
        a. they were natives   c. they like the climate
        b. they were brought as slaves   d. they came to seek gold

1.012   The hired wage earner and the small farm owner are part of the new
        _____ .
        a. slums   c. rich elite
        b. revolution   d. middle class

1.013   The first division of settlements in Brazil was called _____ .
        a. colonies   c. captaincies
        b. states   d. federalcies

1.014   The name of the dentist who led the early fight for Brazil's freedom from
        Portugal was _____ .
        a. Cabral   c. Tiradentes
        b. São Francisco   d. São Vincente

1.015   Cabral claimed Brazil for _____ .
        a. Japan   c. Canada
        b. Spain   d. Portugal

Match the following words by putting the letter in the blank (each answer, 2 points).

1.016 _____	Sertão Region	a. Lowlands
1.017 _____	gold discovery	b. Highlands
1.018 _____	manioc	c. desert
1.019 _____	southern states	d. Tropic of Capricorn
1.020 _____	Portuguese	e. cities
1.021 _____	king of Portugal	f. cattle
1.022 _____	brazilwood	g. language
1.023 _____	Vargas	h. ground into flour
1.024 _____	Southern Region	i. red dye
1.025 _____	Coastal Plain	j. Kubitschek
1.026 _____	Rio de Janeiro	k. capital for 200 years
1.027 _____	Central	l. flag bearers
1.028 _____	Dom Pedro II	m. King John
1.029 _____	Amazon	n. emperor of Brazil
		o. dictator

Write the correct words in the blanks of these sentences (each numbered item, 6 points).

1.030   The dentist who worked for Brazil's independence from a. _____ _____ was nick-named b. _____ .

1.031   King John ruled Portugal from a. _____ .
He was the father of b. _____ who declared
c. _____ from Portugal.

1.032   Dom Pedro II ruled Brazil for nearly a. _____ years, during which
time he visited the b. _____ . He had to leave office
because of trouble over the c. _____ of slaves.

Write the correct word or words in the blanks (each answer, 2 points).

1.033   The largest city in Brazil is _____ .

1.034   Sugar Loaf Mountain can be seen from the harbor of _____ .

1.035   Brasília is now Brazil's _____ city.

1.036   The chief festival holiday in Brazil is _____ .

1.037   The most popular sport of Brazil is _____ .

1.038   Most industries of Brazil are in or near the city of _____ .

1.039   The city that was once a rubber "boom-town" is _____ .

1.040   An important job that Christian missionaries do in Brazil is

_____ .

Answer *true* **or** *false* (each answer, 1 point).

1.041 _____ Savannas are grasslands.

1.042 _____ Rio de Janeiro was Brazil's capital until 1960.

1.043 _____ A dictator is elected.

1.044 _____ *Ascend* means *to come out of a cave.*

1.045 _____ *Emerge* means *to make able.*

1.046 _____ *Christ, the Redeemer* is a statue near Rio de Janeiro.

1.047 _____ Brasilia is the oldest city in Brazil.

1.048 _____ The Butana Snake Institute is in São Paulo.

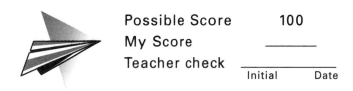

Possible Score   100

My Score   _____

Teacher check   _____

                   Initial   Date

II. COLOMBIA

Colombia was named after Christopher Columbus although he never went there. Colombia is nearer to the United States than any other South American country. It is bounded on the west by the Pacific Ocean, on the north by Panama and the Caribbean Sea, on the South by Ecuador and Peru, and on the east by Venezuela and Brazil. Colombia is important because of its resources, its exports, and its position as a world neighbor to the United States.

The climate of Colombia differs from that of other countries near the equator in that it is cold in many places. In this section of your LIFEPAC, you will be learning about Colombia's regions, its geography, people, history, and cities.

☐   **Review these objectives.**

1.   To discuss the geography of Colombia;

2.   To tell about the wildlife of Colombia;

3.   To discuss the people of Colombia;

4.   To state the major events of history in Colombia;

5.   To name major cities of Colombia;

6.   To name major industries of Colombia; and

7.   To describe present-day Colombia.

GEOGRAPHY

Three mountain ridges start at the west of Colombia and spread inward. They extend from north to south and are a part of the Andes Mountain Range that runs along the western coast of South America. They divide the country into eastern, central, and western regions. Between the mountains are lush valleys.

Climate. The top of some of the mountains in Colombia are so cold that people can ski over the equator. The lower

Skiing over the Equator!

mountain ranges have more moderate climates. The seashores are cooled by ocean breezes. At sea level near the equator it is hot. The east and southeast parts of the country have many jungles and forests.

Rivers. Rivers are important as inland waterways for shipping cargo. One of the principal rivers in Colombia is the Magdalena-Cauca. The Magdelena River divides the eastern and central mountain ridges. It forms a fertile valley. The Cauca River divides the central mountain range and the western ridge, forming another great valley. The Cauca actually is a branch of the Magdalena. However, the two do not join until a few miles before the Magdalena empties into the Caribbean Sea. The Magdalena-Cauca has almost all of the inland commercial water **traffic**. Very little passenger traffic is allowed. Paddle-wheel boats were once used, but more modern boats are now used. The Amazon River, the Putumoya River on the south border of Colombia, and the Orinoco River, which forms part of the boundary between Colombia and Venezuela to the east, are also important waterways.

Crocodile

Wildlife. Many interesting animals such as iguanas, armadillos, monkeys, and deer are found in Colombia. The capybara, a member of the mouse family that is about the size of a medium dog, is one of the more unique animals. Other animals that have their homes in the jungles are the jaguar, the puma, and the wild hog.

Man-eating piranhas live in the river waters along with crocodiles and small tropical fish, similar to those in home aquariums, and six-foot long bait fish, such as Salmon, trout, and catfish.

Ocean life includes marlin, sailfish, dolphin, tuna, lobster, squid, oyster, haddock, barracuda, and sea bass. Many sportsman go to the water near Colombia to deep-sea fish.

Toucans, heron, hummingbirds, and other exotic birds are numerous in the jungle. Migratory birds from the Yukon spend the winter in Colombia.

Resources. Colombia is rich in resources. Emeralds, platinum, and gold used in fine jewelry and rich ornaments form part of the mineral resources. Salt and oil also are valuable resources.

In growing crops Colombia has "four-story" agriculture. Bananas, sugar, cacao, and cotton are raised in the tropical area from sea level to the 3,000-foot level. From 3,000 to 7,000 feet, the air is cool and just right for coffee growing. Coffee is one of Colombia's major exports. From 7,000 to 10,000 feet the air is cold. Apples and potatoes grow well at that height. Above 10,000 feet the air is very cold and barren, and the land is used for grazing. Cattle, raised on the grass-covered plains called the *llanos*, are used for both beef and leather. Sheep thrive in the high country.

Toucan

Do these map-study activities.

2.1   Use parentheses ( ) to mark on the map in the back of this LIFEPAC the three mountain ranges of Colombia.

2.2   Find the Magdalena River and the Cauca River on a large map. Mark them in their correct location on the LIFEPAC map. Mark the southern and eastern borders where the Amazon, Putumayo, and Orinoco rivers are located.

Write the correct answer in the blank.

2.3   The river that divides the west ridge of mountains from the central ridge is the _____ River.
        a. Mississippi   c. Magdalena
        b. Cauca

2.4   The river that divides the east ridge from the central ridge is the
         _____ River.
         a. Cauca   c. Magdalena
         b. Rio Grande

2.5   Coffee is grown _____.
         a. from 3,000 to 7,000 feet   c. from 7,000 to 10,000 feet
         b. at sea level

2.6   In between the mountain ranges are _____.
         a. savannas   c. barren desert
         b. fertile valleys

2.7   The Magdalena River empties into the _____.
         a. Pacific Ocean   c. Caribbean Sea
         b. Bay of Pigs

2.8   The type of cargo carried on the Magdalena and Cauca rivers is
         _____.
         a. vacation excursions   c. military troops
         b. commercial freight

2.9   The river that borders Venezuela is the _____.
         a. Orinoco   c. Amazon
         b. Putumayo

Complete the lists.

2.10   List the type of wildlife found in Colombia under the correct heading.

                              Animals
         a. _____   d. _____
         b. _____   e. _____
         c. _____   f. _____

                         River and Sea Animals
         g. _____   o. _____
         h. _____   p. _____
         i. _____   q. _____
         j. _____   r. _____
         k. _____   s. _____
         l. _____   t. _____
         m. _____   u. _____
         n. _____   v. _____

                              Birds
         w. _____   y. _____
         x. _____   z. _____

Complete this activity.

2.11   On a separate piece of paper, draw a mountain. Label at each level, the crops grown for that elevation. Be sure to label the elevations—3,000 feet, 7,000 feet, or 10,000 feet.

Teacher check _____
                                    Initial   Date

Write the correct answers in the blanks.

2.12   Three minerals used for jewelry are a. _____ ,
        b. _____ , and c. _____ .

2.13   Cattle can be used for a. _____ and b. _____ .

2.14   A resource from the rivers and ocean is _____ .

2.15   A product Colombia has in abundance that is used at nearly every meal
        everywhere is _____ .

PEOPLE

Since the time of the Spanish *conquistadors,* many people in Colombia have spoken some form of Spanish. For this reason Spanish is the official language of the country. The people of Colombia, like the people of Brazil, have descended from many different races. Their citizens are also divided into classes, much as they are in Brazil.

As of 1988, 31 million people lived in Colombia. The population is dropping in the hot jungle area, but is growing in the areas of the seashore and mountain cities.

Race. The ancient Indians are important to the history of Colombia. To make gold sculpture, they used hammers and waxes much as modern sculptors do. They raised their earth in neat ridges, mounds, and dips. This arrangement may have helped in growing better crops.

Today's Indians are important, too. Most of them live to the north and to the west. The *Chibcha,* who live near Bogotá, are miners and makers of useful items. The *Quimbaya* and *Carib* date back before written history. They have always been weavers of textiles and hammocks. They are more artistic than the Chibcha.

Descendants of the Spanish *conquistadors* (conquerors), as well as Blacks descended from the slaves brought over from Africa, live in Colombia today. Seventy-five out of a hundred people living in Colombia are of mixed descent. The mestizos are of Indian and Spanish descent. The mulattos are of Black and white descent.

Social class. The people who are most powerful in Colombia are the *Creoles.* They are the direct, pure-blooded descendants of the early Spanish upper class. (*Creole* has other meanings in other parts of the world.) They have, through the years, controlled most of the country's commerce, social functions, and politics. The remainder of the population form the non-*Creole* class. This class includes the poor and the Indians. A middle class is slowly **emerging** in Colombia, just as it is in Brazil.

Food, clothing, and shelter. In the cities, families eat much as they do in other cities. Coffee is sold on the streets from sidewalk **vendors**. In rural areas diet is meager and usually includes rice, potatoes, manioc, and corn. Armadillo cooked in its shell, iguana, and fried ants are some of the special dishes served.

People of the large cities dress much as we do. Throughout Colombia, however, many people wear the *ruana*, a kind of poncho made from a large, square piece of cloth, wool, or cotton with a slit in the middle so that it can be put over the head. *Ruanas* are worn by men, women, and children for all occasions. They can double as a blanket, a pillow, or even a tablecloth. Some districts have specified colors for *ruanas*. Everyone in these districts wears the same color.

The very rich of Colombia live on fine estates. Professional people, such as doctors, lawyers, and architects, have good homes. The poor live in the city slums in lean-tos and in other makeshift dwellings.

Ruana

 Write the correct letter and word in the blank.

2.16	gold	_____	a. earth ridges
2.17	ancient Indians	_____	b. *conquistadores*
2.18	*Chibcha*	_____	c. miners
2.19	conquerors	_____	d. official language
2.20	Blacks	_____	e. sculpture
2.21	Spanish	_____	f. 75%
2.22	mixed descent	_____	g. 25%
			h. slaves

 Circle the correct answer.

2.23   In Colombia armadillo is _____ .
       a. cooked in the shell   b. eaten raw
       c. never eaten

2.24   The national dress of Colombia is _____ .
       a. pants and vest   b. *ruanas*
       c. blouses

2.25   The poor in Colombia live in _____ .
       a. nice houses   c. makeshift dwellings
       b. caves

HISTORY & GEOGRAPHY

GEOGRAPHY

605

LIFEPAC TEST

80 / 100

Name _____

Date _____

Score _____

HISTORY & GEOGRAPHY 605: LIFEPAC TEST

Match these items (each answer, 2 points).

1.	_____	Simón Bolívar	a. Brazilian soccer player
2.	_____	John	b. largest animal of South America
3.	_____	cruel	c. mountain of iron
4.	_____	Pelé	d. king of Portugal
5.	_____	isolated	e. strengthened for defense
6.	_____	tapir	f. banana-like fruit
7.	_____	Balboa	g. Great Liberator
8.	_____	vendor	h. set apart
9.	_____	"Cerro Bolivar"	i. pitiless
10.	_____	plantain	j. salesman
11.	_____	*Tiradentes*	k. Atlantic Ocean
12.	_____	fortified	l. Pacific Ocean
			m. Brazilian freedom fighter

Circle the correct answer (each answer, 2 points).

13. Stilt houses protect from _____ .
    a. water   c. heat
    b. high winds   d. enemies
14. Aluminum comes from _____ .
    a. salt mines   c. rocks
    b. iron ore   d. bauxite
15. The French Institute of Tropical America studies _____ in French Guiana.
    a. soil and ocean water   c. South American Airlines
    b. disease   d. snakes
16. For years the French used French Guiana for _____ .
    a. a vacation paradise   c. animal experiments
    b. scientific study   d. a penal colony
17. From 3,000 to 7,000 feet, the people of Colombia grow _____ .
    a. sugar cane   c. bananas
    b. apples   d. coffee
18. The name of the mountain in Rio de Janiero's harbor is _____ .
    a. Mt. Brazilia   c. Mt. Nebo
    b. Sugar Loaf Mountain   d. Corcovado Mt.
19. The major export of Suriname is _____ .
    a. iron   c. orange juice
    b. bauxite   d. salt water

20.   Colombia residents live mostly _____ .
        a. in mountain cities and sea coasts   c. in the jungles
        b. in the valleys   d. there part time

21.   The early conquerors were chiefly looking for _____ .
        a. land   c. pearls
        b. gold   d. Indians

22.   Venezuela and Colombia finally rid themselves of the Spanish at the

        _____ .
        a. battle of Carabobo   c. battle of the Bulge
        b. battle of Bunker Hill   d. battle of Bolivia

Complete these statements (each answer, 3 points).

23.   The capital of Brazil is _____ .

24.   The capital of Colombia is _____ .

25.   The capital of Venezuela is _____ .

26.   The capital of Guyana is _____ .

27.   The capital of Suriname is _____ .

28.   The capital of French Guiana is _____ .

29.   The National Front in Colombia was an agreement on how the
        _____ would be elected.

30.   The National Front of Colombia also established rules for filling
        governmental _____ .

31.   Simón Bolívar died in the year _____ .

32.   The name of the early liberator of Colombia who planted more "seeds of
        democracy" than Bolívar did was _____ .

Answer *true* **or** *false* (each answer, 1 point).

33. _____ The capybara is a plant.

34. _____ *El Dorado* means *chief of gold.*

35. _____ *Tiradentes* means *"tooth-puller."*

36. _____ Fiction is fact.

37. _____ Most people in South America live in jungles.

38. _____ The colonial period of a country is a time of growth.

39. _____ Plantains are banana-like fruits.

40. _____ Manioc is a root.

41. _____ Brazil had the first airline.

42. _____ The language of Brazil is Portuguese.

Match the date to the event (each answer, 2 points).

43. _____ April 22, 1500   a. Brazil's Independence Day
44. _____ July 20, 1810   b. Venezuela's Independence Day
45. _____ September 7, 1822   c. Simón Bolívar's birthday
46. _____ July 5   d. Cabral discovered Brazil
47. _____ July 24   e. Guiana's Independence Day
                                   f. Colombia's Independence Day

Define these words (each answer, 3 points).

48.   buccaneer   _____

49.   llano   _____

NOTES

2.26   On the streets in Colombia, vendors sell _____ .
        a. soda pop   c. popcorn
        b. coffee
2.27   Colombian doctors live in _____ .
        a. very small houses   c. good homes
        b. apartments
2.28   The tribes that date back before written history are the Quimbaya and
        _____ .
        a. Carib   c. Mestizos
        b. Chibcha
2.29   The population centers of Columbia are now _____ .
        a. on islands   c. in hot jungles
        b. on seashores and mountains   d. in lush valleys

HISTORY

The story of El Dorado, the long colonial period, and the first moves for independence are all important to Colombia's history. Simón Bolívar was the Great Liberator. His general, Santander, encouraged democracy.

El Dorado. El Dorado, the chief of gold, is a famous figure in South American legend. Many years ago, in ancient times, lived a *Chibcha* Indian chief who was heartbroken. Several times a year he would cover himself with gold dust. Then he would go down to the lake to wash it off. He and his subjects threw gold treasures into the lake. *Conquistadores* looked all over South America for El Dorado and his lake, but never found them. Many have sought this lake and its treasures. Some think that Colombia's Lake Guatavita, in the crater of an old volcano, *might* be the "lake of gold."

Early conquistadores. Bastidas founded the oldest settlement in the Western Hemisphere, Santa Maria, in 1525. Later a man who accompanied him, Vasco Nunez de Balboa, discovered the Pacific Ocean at the Isthmus of Panama in 1533. Francisco Pizarro explored western South America. An explorer named Quesada went into the interior of the country in 1536, founding Bogotá and New Granada, which grew to present-day Colombia. Conquerors were allowed by their mother country to rule, like kings, any territory that they discovered. Thus, a series of separate city-states grew.

Colonial period. At the beginning every country has a lengthy period in which its new colonies try to grow. This period is called the colonial period. In Colombia this period lasted from 1550 to about 1810. Indians worked for nothing for *patrons* or landowners. They had to give crops to their patrons as tribute. During this time **buccaneers** roamed the seas looting and murdering, especially along the Caribbean coast. In 1717 the **viceroyalty** of New Granada, was established by Spain. It was composed of Venezuela, Ecuador, Panama, and Colombia. By 1794 faint movements in the direction of freedom were made. At this time Antonio Narino, a writer, stirred up the people and was expelled to Africa.

Spain gave the colonies the official Spanish language, literature, a printing press, and the Royal Library of Santa Fe.

Complete this activity.

Read the paragraph. Decide what is Fact, Fiction, or Opinion. The story of El Dorado is part fact, part fiction, and part opinion. Study these definitions.

(1) A fact is something that is true.

(2) Fiction is a made-up story.

(3) Opinion is a view based upon given information.

A *Chibcha* Indian chief probably lived once who was heartbroken over the death of his wife. He and his tribesmen followed burial rites that involved offerings of gold. The fact still hidden is where this event happened. Fiction enters in when natives began to tell tall stories about how much gold there was. They made up all kinds of places where the gold might be. They exaggerated to the early explorers how easy it would be to find it. The explorers came to the opinion that a treasure worth looking for existed. They talked kings and queens of Europe into financing their search for gold. They plundered the land of South America, sometimes killing the natives. They did it all because of the opinion they had formed based on the stories of El Dorado. Perhaps they should have searched for the facts.

Complete these sentences with the correct answers.

2.30   The facts of the El Dorado story are that an a. _____
        probably lived who made offerings of b. _____ in a lake to
        his dead c. _____ . We do not know d. _____ this
        event happened.

2.31   The fictional parts of the story of El Dorado were the many stories people
        made up about how a. _____ gold there was, b. _____
        _____ it was and how c. _____ it would be to find.

2.32   The opinion of the *conquistadores* was that a a. _____
        b. _____ looking for existed.

Write the correct answers in the blanks.

2.33   The colonial period of a country is the period in which its new colonies
        try to _____ .

2.34   In Colombia this period was approximately from _____ to 1810.

2.35   During this time a. _____ worked for
        b. _____ for their c. _____ . They had
        to give crops they raised as d. _____ .

2.36   The Viceroyalty of New Granada was made up of
        a. _____ , b. _____ ,
        c. _____ , and Colombia.

2.37   Antonio Nariño was the first man to stir up the people for
        a. _____ from b. _____ .

Move for independence. On July 20, 1810, a **junta** of colonists set themselves up to govern the "United Province of New Granada." They gave this name to the old viceroyalty. July 20 is considered Colombia's Independence Day. The city-state of Cartagena declared its independence in 1811. Before long, however, the Spanish forces now free from fighting Napoleon in Europe put all their energies into recapturing the South American rebel countries. Once again Cartagena was in Spanish hands, as were all the countries of the United Province.

Simón Bolívar
The Great Liberator

The Great Liberator. The Great Liberator, not only of Colombia but of several South American countries, was Simón Bolívar. He was only 5' 6" tall. Along with General Francisco Santander, he defeated the Spanish in 1819. He proclaimed the United Province a republic and was named its first president with Santander as his vice-president. Bolívar ruled the Republic powerfully. He was sometimes considered a tyrant. He was often away liberating other countries from Spanish rule. One of these countries, Bolivia, was named after him. In 1829 and 1830 Venezuela and Ecuador broke away

from Bolívar and from the Republic, leaving only Colombia and Panama. Bolívar was **banished**. He died in the Colombian city of Santa Marta at the home of friends in 1830. Though his people were often angry with him, he has become a great hero because he risked so much to free the countries from Spain.

Conflict of ideas. Bolívar had ruled Colombia much like a king. Santander, who became president after Bolívar died, planted many seeds of democracy. For more than one hundred years since that time, two ideas have been at war with each other in Colombia. One idea, held by the powerful rich, was that Colombia needed a ruling class. The other idea, believed by practically everyone else in the country, was that laws and working conditions must be changed for the sake of the general good. The parties holding these opposing opinions have had many serious battles because the poor far outnumber the rich.

By 1958 everyone in the country was tired of wars and wanted to settle down. The National Front, an agreement that for the next sixteen years the president would be elected from alternate parties, was formed. One of the two parties would serve for four years, the other for the next four years, and so on. All government offices would be equally divided between members of both parties. After sixteen years both parties could run **candidates** for election. In January, 1982 the President of Columbia was chosen from the Liberal Party.

Recent historical facts. In 1903 with the help of the United States President, Theodore Roosevelt, Panama split from Colombia. In 1915 the Panama Canal was built. In 1907 the first textile industry was in Medellín. In 1912 the first automobiles were brought to Colombia. The first airline in all the Americas flew out of Colombia as early as 1919. In 1922 commercial oil production began. In 1931 CAJA, a bank that gives loans to small investors, was established starting Colombia in the direction of helping the "little people."

In 1981, a large band of citizen fighters seized a southern province and bombed the Presidential Palace.

Democratic elections were held in May 1990. Cesar Gavaria Trujillo became president.

Match these words or phrases.

2.38 _____ a *junta*
2.39 _____ United Province of New Granada
2.40 _____ July 20, 1810
2.41 _____ Cartagena
2.42 _____ Napoleon

a. European general
b. a principal city-state
c. U. S. President
d. a new name for the viceroyalty
e. Colombia's Independence Day
f. council

Write the correct answers in the blanks.

2.43 Simón a. _____ is considered the Great
b. _____ of South America because he was the one
who finally c. _____ and the d. _____ .
He was helped by General e. _____ . Bolívar was the first
f. _____ of the new g. _____
of New Granada. h. _____ was the i_____ -president.
Bolívar was often considered a j. _____ by people who
did not like him. He was also away k. _____ other
countries. In 1829-1830 l. _____ and m. _____
broke away from the Republic. Bolívar was n. _____ .
He died in Santa Maria in o. _____ . Through the years he has
become a great p. _____ .

Complete these activities.

2.44 Tell in your own words the difference in the two ideas that have kept the Colombian people divided.
a. _____
b. _____

2.45 In 1958 Colombia formed the National Front. How did this agreement help settle their argument at least for the next sixteen years?
a. _____
b._____

CITIES

Cities have become centers of population and industry in Colombia, just as they have in Brazil and most other South American countries.

Bogotá. Bogotá, the capital of Colombia, was established in 1838 on the eastern ridge of mountains. It usually has a constant temperature of 59°F. The altitude of 8,600 feet sometimes gives visitors breathing problems. Bogotá is a modern city, but it has a lovely old section of historic buildings. Of interest are the Gold Museum, which exhibits many art works of the ancient Indians, and the Salt Cathedral, an underground church that has been carved from a mountain of salt.

Medellín. Medellín is located on the western ridge of mountains north of Bogotá. It has a steady temperature of 70°F and an altitude of 5,000 feet. Medellín was noted for textiles, the first industry in Colombia. Many industries besides textiles are found there today. Orchids that grow everywhere make Medellin a very pretty spot.

Orchids

Seaports. Cartegena is a major seaport on the Caribbean Sea. It was captured by the English pirate Sir Francis Drake in 1585. After that the city built a wall to protect itself against attacks by Henry Morgan, a later pirate, and against other buccaneers in the 1700's. Seventeen miles of the wall still stands.

Leticia is located in the extreme southeast corner of Colombia by the Amazon River. It is a center for exporting zoo animals. A great many hunters go there.

Other Caribbean seaports are important because they are trade centers. Barranquilla is located at the mouth of the Magdalena River. Santa Marta, where Bolívar died, is a banana shipping port to the east.

Pacific ports include Buenaventura, which is probably the most important Colombian port. It is located about halfway down the west coast and is an important oil exporting center. Tumaco, farther south on the west coast, is also an oil exporting center.

Do this map-study activity.

2.46   Locate on the map the cities you read about in these paragraphs. Label them. Label also the Pacific Ocean, the Caribbean Sea, and Panama.

Do this exercise.

2.47 Next to the name of the city write the name of its chief industry, if one has been mentioned. Then write one interesting fact that you have read about that city.

a. Bogotá - _____

b. Medellín - _____

c. Cartegena - _____

d. Barranquilla - _____

e. Santa Marta - _____

f. Buenaventura - _____

g. Tumaco - _____

h. Leticia - _____

COLOMBIA TODAY AND TOMORROW

Today Colombia has many organizations that are helping the poor to have a better way of life. The National Federation of Coffee Growers, founded in 1927, teaches workers to choose a better diet, to plant gardens, and to raise chickens. The federation also pipes in water and electrical power. Most of these workers live on large coffee plantations.

CAJA, the bank that gives loans for small businesses and farms, has **enabled** many to go into business for themselves. The Ministry of Public Health, the United States Peace Corps, and the Protestant missionaries are all trying to help people in the remote areas of the country.

Transportation and communication. Transportation in Colombia is chiefly by air. *Air Avianca*, established in 1919, flies at least two million passengers each year. Other airlines, air taxis, helicopters, and **hydroplanes** are important ways of transportation in Colombia. An effort is being made to improve the country's highway systems. The Pan-American Highway branches out over parts of Colombia.

Communications have improved. By 1968 telephones had reached most towns even in the back country. Thirty-seven major newspapers publish the news. Radio stations and television sets are also popular.

Religion and schools. Colombia is still mainly Roman Catholic and the Protestant church has very little activity there. Grade schools in Colombia are now run mostly by the government and by the public rather than by the church. Children attend school from eight in the morning to noon, take a break from noon until two, and continue school from two until four in the afternoon. Their summer vacation is from November to February because Colombia, like Brazil, is south of the equator where the seasons are just the opposite of those in North America. "School of the air" on the radio also provides education. About thirty-five out of one hundred people in Colombia still cannot read.

Answer these questions.

2.48   What does it mean when we say "wealth is not evenly distributed"?
_____

2.49   What is the name of the organization that helps workers on the large coffee plantations? _____

2.50   What does CAJA do? _____

Write a paper.

2.51   If you were a child in Colombia, your life probably would be different. Find books in your library that tell about Colombia. Read about things that children in Colombia might do. Then write a one-page paper telling what it would be like to be a child in Colombia. Use your own paper. Hand the paper in to your teacher when you finish.

Teacher check _____

                   Initial   Date

Review the material in this section to prepare for the Self Test. The Self Test will check your understanding of this section and will review the first section. Any items you miss on this test will show you what areas you need to restudy.

SELF TEST 2

Circle the correct answer (each answer, 2 points).

2.01   The Gold Museum of Bogotá _____ .
a. is lined with gold   c. was bought with gold
b. exhibits gold treasures   d. has golden floors

2.02   Bolivar died _____ .
a. before he became president   c. at the height of his career
b. in a fit of anger   d. shortly after he was banished

2.03   In Brazil to get to São Paulo from Rio de Janeiro one would have to travel

_____ .
a. south   c. east
b. north   d. west

2.04   The sentence "wealth is not distributed evenly," means that _____ .
a. wealth is for men only   c. no dollar bills are made
b. children do not get allowances   d. a few people have most of the
                                        money

2.05   Between the mountain ridges of Colombia are _____ .
a. fertile valleys   c. deep jungles
b. wide deserts   d. rain forests

2.06	In the colonial days of Colombia, _____ .	
	a. landowners built castles	c. the people prayed at sunset
	b. Indians worked for no pay	d. the farms were like villages
2.07	A *junta* is _____ .	
	a. a group of citizens	c. an animal
	b. military riot	d. an announcement
2.08	*Ruanas* are usually made of _____ .	
	a. grass	c. spunsilk
	b. cotton or wool	d. neither a, b, nor c

Answer *true* **or** *false* (each answer, 1 point).

2.09	_____	The salt cathedral has a roof made of salt.
2.010	_____	The president of Colombia is not elected.
2.011	_____	Bolívar drove out the Spanish armies by himself.
2.012	_____	No moves for Colombian independence were made before Bolívar.
2.013	_____	To *ascend* means to *go down*.
2.014	_____	A dictator is a person who exercises absolute authority.
2.015	_____	The pirates never came on land.
2.016	_____	The present capital of Brazil is Belém.
2.017	_____	*Conquistadores* were interested only in buying land.
2.018	_____	Iguana is used as a food in parts of Colombia.
2.019	_____	Colombia has rid itself of most slums.
2.020	_____	Ancient events have no interest to the present-day people of Colombia.

Match these items (each answer, 2 points).

2.021	_____ CAJA	a. Balboa	
2.022	_____ first airline in the Americas	b. Colombia's Independence Day	
2.023	_____ Leticia	c. walled city	
2.024	_____ Cartegena	d. Bogotá	
2.025	_____ Medellín	e. discovered Brazil	
2.026	_____ Cabral	f. textiles	
2.027	_____ Great Liberator	g. gold sculptors	
2.028	_____ July 20	h. Spain	
2.029	_____ viceroyalty	i. Bolívar	
2.030	_____ pirate	j. bank that means small loans	
2.031	_____ Pacific Ocean	k. zoo animals	
2.032	_____ ancient Colombians	l. *Air Avianca*	
2.033	_____ Magdalena River	m. Sir Francis Drake	
2.034	_____ capital of Colombia	n. freight shipping	
		o. *Tiradentes*	

Answer these questions (each numbered item, 5 points).

2.035   What are two reasons why Bolívar was an unpopular leader?

a. _____

b. _____

2.036   What were two ways in which Colombia solved the problem of friction between two political parties?

a. _____

b. _____

Complete these sentences (each answer, 3 points).

2.037   The official language of Colombia is _____ .

2.038   The city in Brazil that resembles New York City is

_____ .

2.039   The most important river system in Colombia is the

_____ .

2.040   Above 3,000 feet to 7,000 feet, the principal crop in Colombia is

_____ .

2.041   The Caribbean Sea and the Pacific Ocean are separated by the

_____ .

2.042   The language spoken in Brazil is _____ .

Define these words (each answer, 4 points).

2.043   buccaneer _____

2.044   dictator   _____

2.045   savanna   _____

2.046   junta   _____

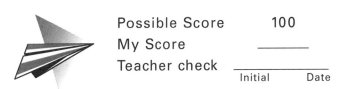

Possible Score   100

My Score   _____

Teacher check   _____

Initial   Date

33

III. VENEZUELA AND THE THREE GUIANAS

In many ways Venezuela has been a land of mystery, because its ports were closed to world travel during the Spanish regime. Many dictators, too, have hindered free communications.

Three comparatively small countries, Guyana, Suriname and French Guiana, lie on the north coast of South America on the Atlantic Ocean. During the last century and up to a few years ago, they were known as British Guiana, Dutch Guiana, and French Guiana.

In this section you will study these countries, their geography, people, history, cities, and industries.

☐ **Review these objectives.**
1. To discuss the geography of Venezuela and the three Guianas,
2. To tell about the wildlife of Venezuela,
3. To discuss the people of Venezuela and the three Guianas,
4. To state the major events of history in Venezuela and the three Guianas.
5. To name major cities of Venezuela and the three Guianas,
6. To name major industries of Venezuela and the three Guianas, and
7. To describe present-day Venezuela and the three Guianas.

☐ **Restudy these words.**

cannibal	fortified	plantains
classify	isolated	smuggler
cruelly		

GEOGRAPHY OF VENEZUELA

Much of Venezuela is covered with mountains and highlands. Venezuela is about 350,000 square miles in area—about twice as large as California. The climate is tropical with dry and rainy seasons.

Venezuela is bordered on the west by Colombia, to the east by Guyana, to the east and south by Brazil, and to the north by 1,800 miles of Caribbean Sea. The country lies entirely north of the equator, in the Torrid Zone. Along its coast lie seventy-two islands. The island of Margarita is the largest of these islands.

Regions. Venezuela has five main regions: the Andes Highlands, the Coastal Plains, the Maracaibo Lowlands, the *Llanos*, and the Guiana Highlands. Most people live in the Andes Highlands. These mountains are in the north and the west of the country, bordering Colombia, and along the coastline. Venezuela has the same four-level agricultural system that Colombia has.

The capital of Venezuela, Caracas, is located on the Coastal Plain, 3,000 feet into the coastal mountains spreading up from the coast. The Coastal Plain is barely fifty miles wide at its widest point.

The Maracaibo Lowlands area contains the Maracaibo Basin and Lake Maracaibo. Lake Maracaibo is the largest natural lake in the world and the center of the petroleum industry.

The *Llanos*, or plains, cover the center of the country. These plains are 600 miles wide and 200 miles long. They are covered with high grasses, jungle, bushy trees, and palms.

The Guiana Highlands are east and south of the Orinoco River. They cover nearly half of the country and are largely unexplored. Angel Falls, the world's highest waterfall, was discovered accidentally by an airplane pilot. In the middle of the jungle, a large plateau called the *Gran Sabana* rises abruptly to heights between 1,500 and 3,000 feet above sea level.

Rivers. Venezuela has more than one thousand rivers. The major river is the Orinoco, which divides the country in half and has been dredged so that ships can travel inland for six hundred miles. The Orinoco's many tributaries are important in supplying hydroelectric power. The Negro River is on the southern border

Wildlife. Wildlife exists in great abundance in Venezuela and does not differ much from that found in Brazil. The puma, wild pigs, monkeys, deer, jaguars, and a large water animal, the manatee, are found in the forests. Brilliantly colored birds, including egrets and macaws, are found in the jungles. The world's smallest hummingbird (about the size of a bumble bee) is also found here. Rivers and streams are the homes of electric eels and turtles. Many reptiles including the coral snake, boa constrictor, and the anaconda live near the rivers and jungles.

Resources. The major mineral resource of Venezuela is petroleum. This resource provides the country with its main source of revenue. Petroleum is found mostly in Lake Maracaibo, but some is exported from the eastern Llanos. Iron is found in the eastern Llanos. In that region "Cerro Bolivar," a whole mountain of iron, was discovered because lightning struck it so often. Venezuela has other resources such as coffee, rice, corn, cotton, sugar, bananas, and sisal for rope.

Oil wells in Lake Maracaibo

Match these activities.

3.1	_____	area of Venezuela	a. plateau
3.2	_____	Caribbean seacoast	b. large water animal
3.3	_____	large island	c. mountain of iron
3.4	_____	petroleum center	d. Angel Falls
3.5	_____	high waterfall	e. 350,000 sq. miles
3.6	_____	*Gran Sabana*	f. Lake Maracaibo
3.7	_____	Orinoco River	g. large land animal
3.8	_____	manatee	h. hydroelectric power
3.9	_____	anaconda	i. Margarita
3.10	_____	"Cerro Bolivar"	j. 1,800 miles long
			k. reptile

Complete this map-study activity.

3.11   On the map at the back of this LIFEPAC, show the five regions of Venezuela. Draw and label these rivers: Orinoco and Negro. Locate and label Lake Maracaibo. Show the location of the Andes Mountains by the use of parentheses ( ).

Complete these statements.

3.12   Venezuela has more than _____ rivers.

3.13   The _____ River divides the country in half.

3.14   People can bring ships up the Orinoco River for a distance of
a. _____ miles because the river has been
b. _____ .

3.15   The Orinoco River and its tributaries are important in providing _____ power.

3.16   A river of Venezuela's southern border is the _____ .

Do this activity.

3.17   Choose one of the animals, birds, or reptiles mentioned in the text on wildlife. Refer to reference books and write two or three paragraphs about the one you choose.

Teacher check _____

                                 Initial   Date

PEOPLE OF VENEZUELA

In 1977 twelve and one-half million people lived in Venezuela. These people live primarily in the Andes Highlands and the Coastal Plain. People are divided by race and by class in Venezuela as they are in other South American countries.

Race and class. The Indians are important to Venezuelan history because a great share of the population has been and is made up of *mestizos*—persons of Indian and Spanish descent. The *Timote* Indians lived in neat villages built around a square with a temple in the middle. Their houses were made of stone. The Chakes are still fiercely protective of their land, and often shoot oil workers in Lake Maracaibo with bow and arrow. The *Quirquire* have always lived in stilt houses, not only to keep out of the water, but to avoid ground animals and insects. The *Carib* Indians had one tribe, the *Caracas*, that **fortified** their villages with tall fences and tried to fight off the Spanish in the early days. Today 2 per cent of the landowners still own 75 per cent of the Venezuelan land. This land is worked by the poor. The Agarian Reform Laws of 1960, however, turned over thousands of acres to individual families. Many men and women are now employed as factory workers with good wages. As in other countries, Venezuela is developing a middle class.

**Stilt house found
in jungles and lakes.**

Food. Plantains, a banana-like food is a staple food in Venezuela along with manioc. For feast days, however, they cook delicious dishes.

Choose words from the Word Bank to complete this paragraph.

─── WORD BANK ───

Timote	mestizos	village
Chake	arrows	fortified
Quirquire	insects	stone
Spanish	per cent	landowners
individuals	wages	temple

3.18   The native Indians are important to Venezuelan history. Most of the people are a. _____ . One tribe always had a b. _____ in the center of the c. _____ . Their houses were made of d. _____ . These were the e. _____ Indians. The f. _____ lived in stilt houses to protect them from water, ground animals, and g. _____ . The h. _____ tribe still shoot the oil workers with i. _____ . In the early days, the *Caracas*

j. _____ their villages to ward off the
k. _____ . Two per cent of the l. _____
still own 75 m. _____ of the land. New laws have given
acres to n. _____ and many others are working in
factories for good o. _____ .

HISTORY OF VENEZUELA

The history of Venezuela follows a pattern like that of other countries. Early conquerors, attempts at freedom, and progress toward democracy are found in Venezuelan history as in the history of most South American countries.

Conquerors. All the conquerors who came to Venezuela came in the name of Spain. On his third voyage to America in 1498, Columbus sailed by the coast of Venezuela and called it "Earthly Paradise." Ojeda and Amerigo Vespucci saw the stilt houses in Lake Maracaibo and thought they looked like Venice, Italy. So they gave Venezuela its name, "Little Venice." Early settlers found priceless pearls in the oysters around the Venezuelan islands in the Caribbean. They **cruelly** forced the Indians to dive for oysters from dawn to dusk and many of them died. The oyster beds were all empty in twenty years. In 1528 the king of Spain leased Venezuela to a group of German bankers who were more cruel than the Spaniards when they went on treasure-seeking expeditions. The lease was revoked in 1556. A year later Caracas was founded. Caracas later became the capital of Venezuela. Pirates, many of them English, looted and burned villages from the sixteenth century to the eighteenth century. Partly for this reason Spain forbade Venezuela to trade with any other country until 1777. This action **isolated** the country and encouraged **smugglers**.

Freedom. The desire for freedom in Venezuela, as in other countries, was helped by the American Revolution. The first great leader for freedom was José España. In 1806 Francisco de Miranda, who had fought with George Washington in the United States, started a move for freedom. He had to flee to London, however, but returned later to fight with Bolívar. In 1815, Simón Bolívar liberated Venezuela along with Colombia. More battles were fought before the Spanish were driven out. The battle of Carabobo in 1821 rid both Venezuela and Colombia of Spanish rule forever. Venezuela eventually broke from Colombia and Panama.

Democracy. Because the people were not ready to understand democracy, Venezuela was ruled by dictatorship for 130 years. One dictator, Juan Vincent Gómez, the Tyrant, ruled from 1908 to his death in 1935, a total of twenty-seven years. People danced in the streets after he died and demanded democracy. They were now ready for it. Rómulo Betancourt was inaugurated president in 1959 and a Federal Constitution was adapted. Betancourt held office for a full five years and since then his successors have been freely elected. The citizens of Venezuela are pleased with their new government. President Rafael Calderon was elected in 1994.

Now that they have a chance to rule themselves, Venezuelans would do well to heed the words in Galatians 5:1 "... be not entangled again with the yoke of bondage." This task is one of the Christian missionary: To teach God's plan of Salvation, His mercy and grace, and how God intends for them to do things for themselves.

Complete these sentences.

3.19   All the conquerors came to Venezuela in the name of _____ .

3.20   *Venezuela* means _____ .

3.21   Spain forbade Venezuela to trade with other countries partly to discourage the _____ .

3.22   Columbus called Venezuela " _____ ."

3.23   Pearls were found in the waters of the _____ .

Answer these questions.

3.24   Why did Venezuelans wait 130 years to rid themselves of dictators?
_____

3.25   What was Gómez called? _____

3.26   How many years did Gómez stay in power? _____

3.27   What signs do we have that democracy may last in Venezuela?
_____

CITIES OF VENEZUELA

Caracas is the capital of Venezuela. It is a cool city, 72°F the year round, but its seaport seven miles closer to the sea is hot and humid.

There is much to see in the beautiful city of Caracas. Three places of special interest are the twin towers, the Bolívar Plaza in the center of the city with a statue of Simón Bolívar on his horse, and Mount Avila where a large hotel has been built. The only way to reach it is by means of a five-mile cable car ride to the top of the mountain. Recently, this hotel was bought by a United States company.

Maracaibo, a city of palms, is the second largest city. It became rich from the oil in the Maracaibo Lake. Oil derricks have been built right in the lake to pump oil.

La Ascunción on Margarita Island was founded in 1824 and was once the center of the big pearl industry. Now tourists and others dive for pearls for recreation.

Do this exercise.

3.28   Three Venezuelan cities are mentioned in the paragraphs you just read. Copy the names of the cities and write two facts about each of them.

a. _____   b. _____   c. _____
1. _____   1. _____   1. _____
2. _____   2. _____   2. _____
_____   _____   _____

INDUSTRY

Although the manufacturing and exporting of petroleum products is the main industry of Venezuela, many people work in construction. Important iron deposits have led the government to build steel plants. Coal, diamonds, copper, and asbestos are also mined. Other leading products manufactured in Venezuela include textiles, clothing, chemicals, foods, and drugs.

Complete this activity.

3.29 Look up the subject of petroleum in an encyclopedia or other source book. On a separate sheet of paper, write, in your own words, two or three paragraphs about it. Include some of the by-products made from it.

Teacher check _____

Initial   Date

RECREATION

Games and sports are popular in Venezuela. *Futbol* is the national game. *Futbol,* what Americans call soccer, is played by everyone. Baseball, water sports, bicycling, and horse racing are also popular. Many cities have bull rings that are crowded with spectators during the months from November to February.

Most holidays are of a religious nature. The birth of Jesus is celebrated on December 25. Children exchange gifts twelve days later on Three King's Day. Easter is also an important holiday. In some villages a straw-filled dummy figure of Judas is stuffed with firecrackers and tied to the back of a donkey that is led through the streets. At last the false Judas is raised to the top of a pole and the exploding firecrackers delight everyone in the crowd.

Other national holidays which Venezuelans celebrate are the birthday of their national hero, Simón Bolívar, July 24, and their Independence Day, July 5.

Match these words.

3.30 _____ soccer   a. July 5
3.31 _____ Jesus' birth   b. *futbol*
3.32 _____ Simón Bolívar   c. January 6
3.33 _____ Independence Day   d. December 25
3.34 _____ bullfights   e. November-February
                                       f. July 24

VENEZUELA TODAY AND TOMORROW

Schools are becoming increasingly important and getting better all the time. Many adults attend schools in Venezuela. The cities have many libraries. The country is largely Roman Catholic in religion, but Protestant missionaries have been active there, especially in the area around Maracaibo Lake

Airlines are important. Even the smallest town in Venezuela seems to have an airport. The Pan-American Highway branches over the country, but more good roads are needed. Over the Orinoco River is the longest suspension bridge in the world. A concrete bridge spans Lake Maracaibo. Many newspapers, television sets, and telephones can be found throughout the country. Venezuela needs to have more of its people share the wealth of the country. It needs clean water, sanitation in some areas, more doctors, nurses, and hospitals. Venezuela still has to import much of the food it eats.

 Complete these sentences.

3.35   The longest suspension bridge in the world is over the
_____ .

3.36   The most common way to travel in Venezuela is by
_____ .

3.37   Much of Venezuela's food needs to be _____ .

GEOGRAPHY AND PEOPLE OF THE THREE GUIANAS

The climate and geography of the three Guianas are much the same as the countries you have studied. Their populations are concentrated along the seacoast. Bush Blacks, descendants either of runaway slaves or of freed slaves who fled inland, and Indians live in the interior. The Bush Blacks and Indians live in the jungles and in the rain forests—where high trees grow close together. A jungle is full of low trees, bushes, grasses, and vines. The Bush Blacks have set up villages much like their ancestors in Africa. They do woodwork. The *Carib* Indians live near the coast. In early times they were **cannibals**. Daniel Defoe described them in *Robinson Crusoe.* Today they are very civilized. As in other countries, conquerors pillaged the Guianas in a mad search for gold. The coasts of the Guianas were also raided by the buccaneers. Most present day inhabitants of these three countries are of a mixed race.

 Complete these sentences.

3.38   Daniel Defoe wrote _____ .
3.39   The *Carib* Indians were _____ in earlier times.
3.40   Bush Blacks are descendants of slaves who fled _____ .

41

GUYANA

Guyana was acquired by Great Britain in 1616. Its capital, Georgetown, is a very British city. Guyana was a possession of England until 1966 when it was made a free territory. In 1970 all ties to the British were broken. Guyana has large sugar plantations. Bauxite, the metal from which aluminum is made, is an important industry. Famous people of Guyana include "Martyr" John Smith, a missionary who was arrested for teaching the slaves to read. He died in jail. Dr. John Giglioli rid the country of malaria. A number of naturalists in the past two centuries did much to **classify** the plant life of Guyana.

Today Guyana's government is a Republic. In 1992, Cheddie Jagan was elected president.

Write the correct answer in each blank.

3.41   By a. _____ all ties to the b. _____ were broken.

3.42   The large plantations in Guyana raise _____ .

3.43   The metal from which aluminum is manufactured is _____ .

3.44   "Martyr" Smith taught the slaves how to _____ .

3.45   The man who rid the country of malaria was _____ .

3.46   Plant life was classified by _____ .

SURINAME

Suriname was traded in 1667 to the Dutch for a parcel of land in the United States. The Dutch got Suriname and the British got New Amsterdam, the present location of New York City. The capital of Suriname is Paramaribo, a beautiful city with Dutch-style houses and government buildings. During World War II Suriname stood by the Queen of the Netherlands when she had to flee to England. In return for this action, the queen offered Suriname freedom. This freedom came gradually between 1954 and 1975. Suriname has few white people. Since 1975, this country has gone back and forth between military and civilian governments. Democracy has now returned, and President Ronald Venetian was elected in 1991.

The most important language is Dutch. Hindustani is also used extensively because Suriname has a large Hindustani population. Most of the churches in Suriname are Dutch Reformed. All of the three Guianas were taught by the early Dutch settlers how to build dikes, sea walls, and sluice gates to control the ocean. Schools have been important. Nearly everybody, except the Bush Blacks and Indians, can read and write. Suriname's principal export is bauxite. An American orange-juice factory there uses Suriname citrus.

Do this exercise.

3.47   Unscramble these words.

a. eNw sedAtmrma _____

b. ader nda rteiw _____

c. kdeis, waasllse, clsuei, tgesa _____ , _____ ,

_____ ,

d. tcDuh tsrselte _____

e. ndisisantuH _____

FRENCH GUIANA

In the middle of the seventeenth century France acquired French Guiana and soon discovered that it was a worthless parcel of land. France began to send prisoners there and French Guiana soon became a penal colony with a bad reputation. Devil's Island, off the coast of French Guiana, held many famous political prisoners. Other islands also were used for prisons. Less dangerous prisoners were put on the mainland. The prisons were closed in 1946 and people now live in the old prison barracks. In 1946 French Guiana was made a Department (state) of France, and it remains so today. One famous export of French Guiana is spices. Cayenne pepper was named after its capital. The Pasteur Institute went there to study tropical diseases, and the French Institute of Tropical America studies soil and ocean water. Health centers are numerous. In 1965 a Missile and Space Center was established in French Guiana.

Answer these questions.

3.48   What kind of prisoners were sent to Devil's Island?

_____

3.49   What kind of prisoners did they keep on the mainland?

_____

3.50   In what year were the prisons closed?

_____

3.51   In what year was French Guiana made a Department of France?

_____

3.52   What kind of pepper has the same name as the capital of French Guiana?

_____

Writing project.

3.53   Review this section of your LIFEPAC. List the three Guianas on a piece of paper. Write some of the things you have learned about each one such as the capitals of each country, the Pasteur Institute, the Institute of Tropical Diseases, the Space and Missile Center, the dikes and sea walls, the Bush Black, and others. Choose one of the Guianas and look up further information about it. Then write several paragraphs (no less than two) on the subject you have chosen.

Teacher check _____

Initial   Date

Before you take this last Self Test, you may want to do one or more of these self checks.

1. _____ Read the objectives. See if you can do them.
2. _____ Restudy the material related to any objectives that you cannot do.
3. _____ Use the SQ3R study procedure to review the material:
   a. **S**can the sections,
   b. **Q**uestion yourself,
   c. **R**ead to answer your questions,
   d. **R**ecite the answers to yourself, and
   e. **R**eview areas you did not understand.
4. _____ Review all vocabulary, activities, and Self Tests, writing a correct answer for every wrong answer.

SELF TEST 3

Circle the correct answer (each answer, 2 points).

3.01   Even the smallest town in Venezuela has _____ .
        a. a vending machine   c. a statue
        b. an airport   d. a village square

3.02   Seventy-five percent of the land in Venezuela is owned by _____ .
        a. 2% of the people   c. 17% of the people
        b. 75% of the people   d. 10% of the people

3.03   The most important export of Venezuela is _____ .
        a. bananas   c. petroleum
        b. iron   d. nuts

3.04   After Venezuela declared its freedom from Spain, dictators ruled the country for _____ .
        a. 85 years   c. 5 years
        b. 50 years   d. 130 years

3.05   The colonial period of any country is a time of _____ .
        a. growing   c. sleeping
        b. war   d. becoming extinct

3.06   The *ruana* is similar to a _____ .
        a. tablecloth   c. coat
        b. poncho   d. skirt

3.07   Venezuela was given its name because the stilt houses in Lake Maracaibo reminded explorers of _____ .
        a. Venice   c. Lisbon
        b. Paris   d. Hong Kong

3.08   Around Margarita Island the early settlers found a wealth of _____ .
            a. oil   c. gold
            b. grapes   d. pearls
3.09   The Guianas learned how to build dikes and sea walls from the _____ .
            a. Africans   c. Chinese
            b. United States   d. Dutch
3.010   The Indians Robinson Crusoe referred to were _____ .
            a. Carib   c. Navajo
            b. Quirquiri   d. Caracas

Match these terms (each answer, 2 points).
3.01   _____ martyr   a. pirate
3.012   _____ bauxite   b. American orange juice
3.013   _____ Pasteur Institute   c. Bogotá
3.014   _____ El Dorado   d. tropical disease
3.015   _____ Devil's Island   e. malaria
3.016   _____ spice   f. chief of gold
3.017   _____ Suriname citrus   g. Cayenne
3.018   _____ Netherlands   h. *Carib* Indians
3.019   _____ Giglioli   i. French prison
3.020   _____ cannibals   j. cooked in the shell
3.021   _____ Robinson Crusoe   k. Caracas
3.022   _____ buccaneer   l. Cayenne pepper
3.023   _____ Brazil's capital   m. Brasilía
3.024   _____ Colombia   n. aluminum
3.025   _____ Venezuela   o. Paramaribo
3.026   _____ Guyana   p. Daniel Defoe
3.027   _____ Suriname   q. Amazon Lowlands
3.028   _____ French Guiana   r. *Tiradentes*
3.029   _____ Amazon River   s. Queen
3.030   _____ armadillo   t. Georgetown
                                            u. Rev. John Smith

Complete these statements (each answer, 3 points).
3.031   The British traded Suriname for _____ .
3.032   Most of the inhabitants of all three Guianas are of _____ race.
3.033   The interior part of the Guianas is populated by a. _____
            and b. _____ .
3.034   The *Carib* Indians, who were once cannibals, are now _____ .

3.035   "Cerro Bolivar" was discovered in the Guiana Highlands of Venezuela because it was hit so much by _____ .

3.036   In Venezuela hydroelectric power is taken from the _____ River.

3.037   The largest natural lake in the world is _____ Lake.

3.038   The national game of Venezuela is _____ .

3.039   The capital of Venezuela is _____ .

3.040   One hummingbird in Venezuela is about the size of a

_____ .

Answer these questions (each answer, 5 points).

3.041   What is the difference between a rain forest and a jungle?

_____

_____

3.042   Who was the Brazilian president who moved the Capital to Brasília?

_____

Possible Score   100

My Score   _____

Teacher check   _____

Initial   Date

Before taking the LIFEPAC Test, you may want to do one or more of these self checks.

1. _____   Read the objectives. See if you can do them.
2. _____   Restudy the material related to any objectives that you cannot do.
3. _____   Use the SQ3R study procedure to review the material.
4. _____   Review activities, Self Tests, and LIFEPAC vocabulary words.
5. _____   Restudy areas of weakness indicated by the last Self Test.

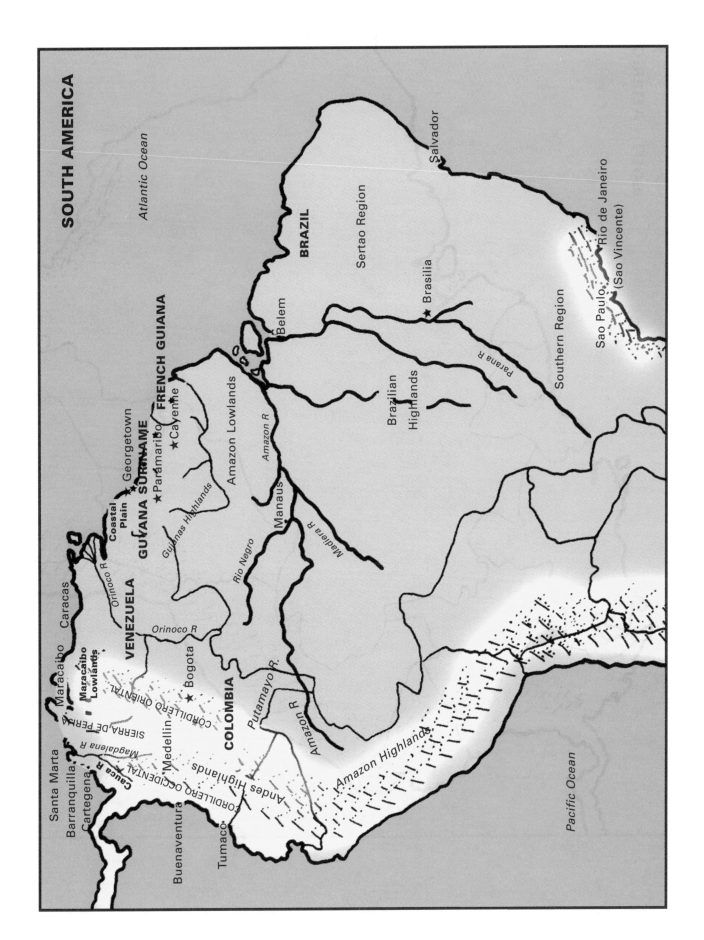

SOUTH AMERICA

Atlantic Ocean

BRAZIL

Sertao Region

Salvador

Rio de Janeiro
(Sao Vincente)

Brasilia

Sao Paulo

Belem

Southern Region

Parana R

Brazilian
Highlands

FRENCH GUIANA

Amazon Lowlands

Amazon R

Georgetown

Cayenne

Paramaribo

SURINAME

GUIANA

Coastal
Plain

Guianas Highlands

Manaus

Madiera R

Orinoco R

Rio Negro

VENEZUELA

Caracas

Orinoco R

Bogota

Putamayo R.

Amazon R

Maracaibo

Maracaibo
Lowlands

COLOMBIA

Medellin

CORDILLERO ORIENTAL

SIERRA DE PERIJA

Santa Marta

Barranquilla

Cartegena

Magdalena R

Cauca R

Andes Highlands

Amazon Highlands

Buenaventura

Tumaco

CORDILLERO OCCIDENTAL

Pacific Ocean

47

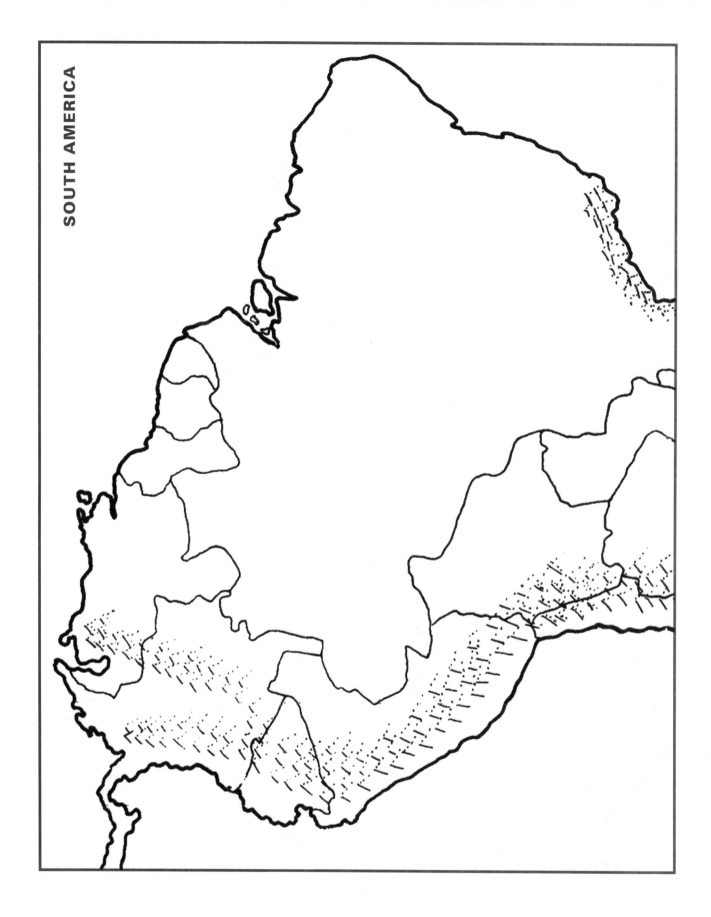

SOUTH AMERICA

Alpha Omega Publications

a division of:

Bridgestone Multimedia Group

Chandler, Arizona

1-800-622-3070